THE BONES OF
MARY ELWES

A SCREENPLAY BY

J B MacCALLUM

Dedicated to

Agnes Walker Chalmers.

FADE IN.

INT. UNDERGROUND STATION. LONDON. 1950S

It is late evening. A dapper BUSINESSMAN, wearing a long coat and carrying a briefcase, is standing close to the edge of the platform in a relatively quiet underground station. There are no more than a dozen others also waiting.

The businessman looks at his watch. A close up shows the time to be 8.55 pm. Further along the platform stands a WOMAN, holding the hand of a four year old GIRL. The girl is looking up at the station ceiling, focusing on something we do not see. Her eyes follow until she is looking at the businessman.

There is a rumble in the tunnel as the train approaches, its white lights piercing the darkness. Suddenly the little girl screams. Just as the businessman looks round to see what is happening he is pushed by an unseen force into the path of the oncoming train.

As horrified passengers look on, we focus on the girl. Looking frightened and bewildered, her mind engaged with something else — something only she can see.

EXT. DISUSED UNDERGROUND STATION. LONDON. NIGHT. PRESENT DAY.

It is 2am. The London Underground system has closed for the night and the power is shut down for maintenance crews.

A large van pulls up and parks outside the pre-war frontage of *BROOM STREET*, an abandoned underground station. Three men, JACK SCANLON, a portly Londoner in his early forties, DION GARDINER, a slim, twenty year old black Londoner and KRZYSZTOF (KRZYS) JURCZAK a 28 year old Polish man, get out of the van.

Jack and Dion approach the entrance which is secured behind a set of padlocked concertina style metal gates. Meanwhile, Krzysztof has opened the rear cargo doors of the van and is pulling out the equipment they will need.

                    DION
     When was the last time this
     place was used?

                    JACK
     Early fifties.

INT. DISUSED UNDERGROUND STATION. NIGHT.

Once inside, Jack and Dion's powerful hard
hat mounted torch beams pierce the pitch
black, partially illuminating the well
preserved Edwardian interior. Both men look
enthralled.

After Jack locates the master switch box,
the whole place is then illuminated by
overhead strip lights.

                    JACK
     At least the lights work.

                    DION
     WOW! This place is well old.

                    JACK
     A hundred and forty years.

                    DION
        And they want to re-open it?

                    JACK
        Just temporarily, whilst
        they upgrade Whitechapel...
        Depending on what state it's
        in of course.

Fifties posters and adverts still adorn the
walls, amusing and interesting both men.
Jack's mobile phone rings. He looks at the
display and answers.

                    JACK
        Marty, where are you?
            (Beat)
        Jesus, you alright?
            (Beat)
        What happened?
            (Beat)
        Alright mate, see you in
        a bit.
            (Hangs up)

Krystoph enters carrying a couple of
portable safety lanterns and associated
equipment, etc.

                    KRZYS
                 (Polish)
          What up with the Marty?

                    JACK
          He's had a bit of trouble.

                    KRZYS
          What sort of troubles?

                    JACK
          Something to do with a woman,
          her angry husband and a
          broken nose.

                    KRZYS
          Is he going to come work?

                    JACK
          He's on his way.

LATER.

With equipment inside, Jack, Dion & Krzysztof stand before large padlocked metal gates that prevent access to stairs, passageways and tunnels that lead below. The dim, flickering strip lighting illuminates more vintage adverts and signs.

The three men descend a spiral staircase that leads down to long passageways. They then walk along a tunnel and go down a number of steps. As they do they come across a row of old advertisements and are amused by the corny text and the £500 guinea asking price of a new 1950s car.

Further down Krzys trips and stumbles. He curses in Polish and gets up.

                    JACK
          You alright?

                    KRZYS
          No worry, I okay.

The men descend further. As they do an eerie, echoing, moaning sound emanates from below.

                    DION
What the was that!

                    JACK
Probably just the wind.

                    DION
Probably?

                    JACK
There's all sorts of strange
sounds down here. You get
used to it.

                    KRZYS
It not sound like wind to me.

                    JACK
Don't you start.

The trio walk down the last dozen or so
steps that lead to the platform entrance.
They notice that there has been a partial
collapse of the masonry above the entrance
leaving large lumps of debris on the floor.

                    DION
Jesus, this is well spooky.

                    KRZYS
Not sure I like.

                    DION
So why did they shut
this place?

                    JACK
Something to do with all
the deaths.

                    DION
Deaths!? What deaths?

                    JACK
Suicides. People jumping
in front of trains.

                    KRZYS
You joke yes?

                    JACK
There was so many it became
known as doom street.

                    DION
Why so many suicides here?

JACK

No one knows. Enough was
enough so they decided to
close it.

KRZYS

So how you know this?

JACK

Wikipedia.

LATER. PLATFORM.

DION

This place is wicked. It's
like going back in time.

KRZYS
(After pause)
I not like. There something
not right.

Krzys takes a mobile phone out of his pocket.

DION

What you on about?

                    KRZYS
        Not sure but I feel in bone.

                    DION
        I can't feel anything.

Krzys looks at the illuminated screen on
his mobile phone. There is no signal.

LATER.

Armed with an HD digital camcorder, Jack is
taking footage of the overall condition of
the station.

                    DION
        What's with the video?

                    JACK
        A picture tells a thousand
        words… Here take this.

Jack hands the camera to Dion then picks
up the receiver of an emergency phone link
that is located in a small recession.

                    JACK (Cont'd)
        Hello... Testing, testing
        one, two, three.
                (Beat)
        Nothing.

He then opens a large pair of rusty creaking
louvered doors that conceal a generator
cupboard. Illuminated by their helmet
lights and the strip lighting, the machine
is covered in dust and spiders webs.

Jack takes the camera back from Dion and
continues to film. Everything he captures is
seriously decayed, rusty and covered in a
gritty dust.

WEST TUNNEL. RAILWAY TRACK.

Krzys is walking into the start of the west tunnel. It is partially illuminated but not far along it becomes pitch black. Krzys switches on his helmet light. He is doing a similar job to Jack, photographically documenting the general state and condition. From deeper in the tunnel he hears a faint scraping. He stops and listens. The scraping is intermittent and appears to be getting louder.

Krzys takes a few tentative steps forward towards the source of the sound, the beam of his helmet torch piercing the pitch black. Again he listens but there is no sound apart from the eerie howl of an underground wind.

Shrugging it off, Krzys continues his work. Moments later he hears the scraping again - only louder. Curious, Krzys walks further into the tunnel and stops to listen again. This time the scraping is followed by what sounds like an eerie human sigh.

                    KRZYS
          Hello...

Krzys takes a couple of flash photos towards the source of the sound. Moments later there is another, slightly louder, sigh.

> KRZYS (Cont'd)
> Is anyone there?

PLATFORM.

Resume Jack and Dion checking and photographing an electrical generator. Suddenly they hear a blood curdling scream from the west tunnel. Ad-lib reaction from both.

> JACK
> WHAT THE FUCK!!

Immediately, Jack grabs his walkie talkie.

> JACK (Cont'd)
> (Into W/T)
> KRZYS, KRZYS... come in -
> over.
> (Beat)
> KRZYS are you alright!?

A few moments later Jack's W/T crackles.

                        KRZYS (Over W/T)
                    (Breathing heavily)
                No, I bloody no alright!

                        JACK
                    (Into W/T)
                Stay put we'll be right over.

WEST TUNNEL.

Jack calls into tunnel.

                        JACK
                    KRZYS!... KRZYS!

After a few anxious moments a clearly
agitated Krzys emerges from the darkness.

                        JACK (Cont'd)
                What the fuck happened?

                        KRZYS
                I get big fright! That
                what happen!

From behind Krzys the illuminated ghostly face of a man suddenly appears. They all jump momentarily before realising it is way laid crew member MARTY BRIDGES, early 40s, with a torch beam held below his chin - sporting a black eye and a sticking plaster over his nose.

> MARTY
>> Jesus, talk about a bunch of drama queens.

Jack and Dion sigh a sigh of relief.

> KRZYS
>> You almost give me attack of heart!

> MARTY
>> It was a joke for fuck sake.

> KRZYS
>> You see me laugh!

> JACK
>> What did you do to him?

                    MARTY
          Nothing... All I did was grab
          his ankle.

                    KRZYS
          In blackness - how I know
          it you, eh! It could be
          giant rat or big snake.

                    MARTY
          Oh yeah big snakes just love
          it down here don't they.
          All that sunshine.

                    KRZYS
          Fucking arsehole.

Jack and Dion look amused.

                    JACK
          So what kept you?

LATER.

All four are sitting on edge of platform having a tea break.

> MARTY
>
> I tell you straight up, she's the best bit of muff I have ever had.

> KRZYS
>
> Muff? What is muff?

> MARTY
>
> Jesus Borat how long you been here. Fanny, pussy.

Krzys still looks confused.

> KRZYS
>
> You mean cat?

> JACK
>
> He means woman.

> KRZYS
>
> Woman. Then why you not say this?... And not be calling me Borat.

                    MARTY
               (After beat)
        Anyway, I tell you she gives
        it like I don't know what.

                    JACK
        Just a shame about her
        husband.

                    KRZYS
        If you have wife, why would
        you sex with other woman?

                    MARTY
        Have you ever seen my wife?
        She makes a monkfish look like
        Natalie Portman.

                    JACK
        And that's putting it kindly.

                    KRZYS
        I don't care, it still no
        excuse to cheat on her. You
        make vow you should stick to
        it.

Our attention is unexpectedly drawn to the entrance of the east tunnel. A dark shadow moves into the tunnel and merges with the dark. Jack catches it out of the corner of his eye.

> DION
> What is it?

> JACK
> (After beat)
> Eh, nothing.

LATER. PLATFORM.

The four men carry on with their individual tasks, etc. Marty is checking the track at the entrance of the east tunnel. As he is working, an eerie shadow morphs near him. Sensing that something is behind him Marty looks round. But, just as he does, the shadowy apparition quickly dissolves, leaving him to shrug it off.

Moments later, one of the overhead strip lights flickers and goes out. Ad-lib comments. Seconds after that another light does the same. Then another and another.

                    JACK
        What the?...

                    KRZYS
              (Curses in Polish)

                    DION
        That's not supposed to happen.

                    KRZYS
        Least there still one left.

As if on cue, the last light dims and
goes out. However, the emergency lanterns
that they have brought with them turn
on automatically.

                    DION
        Shit, now what we going to do?

Ad-lib reaction.

                    MARTY
        That's it then. No strip
        lights, no work... Thank fuck
        for health and safety.

                    DION
        Do we get to knock off?

                    JACK
Well we can't carry on
without proper lighting.
Looks like a job for
the sparkies.

                    MARTY
Early breakfast then
bugger off.

                    JACK
Bugger off! You've not long
got here.

                    MARTY
It's not my fault the
lighting's broke.

                    KRZYS
This crazy. We have lantern
light. In Poland we carry on.

                    MARTY
Thank Christ we're not in
Poland then.

> JACK
>
> Nobody's going to breakfast
> early and no one's buggering
> off. There's plenty work to be
> done elsewhere.

Reaction from Marty. He begrudgingly accepts
Jack's decision.

> JACK (Cont'd)
> Finish up, pick up your gear
> and make your way up top...
> Carefully.

LATER.

Dion has the camcorder. He is taking a few
random shots of the platform area, etc.   As
Krzys approaches.

> DION
> Krzys man. Take one of me
> standing next to this.

Dion hands camera to Krzys, then poses next
to an old style station name on the wall.
(BROOM STREET)

                    DION
        One for Facebook.

                   KRZYS
        I sure you get lot of like.

Suddenly the emergency lantern lights dim
and go off one by one. Now in pitch darkness
they switch on their helmet lights.

                    JACK
            Oh, you've got to be
            kidding me.
                 (To Krzys)
            I thought you said you
            fully charged them.

                   KRZYS
            Not understand. I charge
            all of them for sure. Ask
            the Dion.

                    DION
            He did. The green charge
            light was on all of them.

                    JACK
         They should last five
         hours at least not fifteen
         bloody minutes!

                    KRZYS
         What you want me to say.

                    JACK
         For fuck sake... Right let's
         get out of here.
              (Beat)
         Where's Marty gone?

Jack scans with his head torch. Marty is
nowhere to be seen.

                    JACK(Cont'd)
              (Shouts)
         MARTY!.. Come on, we're
         leaving!

                    MARTY
              (From Distance)
         Okay, I'll just be a minute.

Moments later a loud AAAARRHH! pierces the
dark from Marty's direction. Jack and the
others stop in their tracks.

                    JACK
        MARTY!... You alright mate!?
            (Beat)
        MARTY!... MARTY!
            (To others)
        If he's fucking about I'll
        kill him.

They then hear a feint cry for help.

                    KRZYS
        Here we go. Another
        stupid joke.

                    JACK
        Marty stop fucking about.

They hear another feint cry.

                    DION
        Don't know about you but it
        don't sound like he's joking.

Jack sighs and puts down his kit.

                    JACK
        You two stay here.

As quickly as possible (Under torch light)
Jack moves in direction of Marty.

> MARTY
> (Distressed)
> Jack, help me... I can't
> move! Get an ambulance, get
> an ambulance!

> JACK
> I swear Marty, if you're
> pissing about you will need
> more than a bloody ambulance!

Jack's torch beam casts a light in the
direction of Marty's moans.

Dion and Krzys are waiting by the platform
exit/entrance. Moments later.

> JACK
> KRZYS, DION! GET HERE NOW!!

Krzys and Dion rush towards the light
of Jack's torch. When they arrive they
discover Jack kneeling down on the tracks
next to Marty, who is lying face up with
the lower part of his back bent over one
of the track rails. Ad-lib reaction.

                    KRZYS
        My God what happen!?

                    JACK
        He's fallen on to tracks.
        Don't know how bad but it
        doesn't look too good.
              (Beat)
        Dion, get up top as quick as
        you can. As soon as you get a
        signal call an ambulance.

Dion wastes no time and goes as quickly
as possible.

                    MARTY
              (Barely conscious)
        I, I can't feel my legs.

                    KRZYS
        Just try to stay as still as
        can. You be okay, I sure.

                    JACK
        Jesus... Only a dozy arse
        like you could trip and fall
        onto the bloody tracks.

                    MARTY
              (After beat)
        I didn't trip.
              (Couple of beats)
        Something pushed me...

Nonplussed reaction from Jack and Krzys.

MONTHS LATER.

EXT. TOWN HOUSE. LONDON. NIGHT.

Jack and Krzys are standing at the front
door of a large townhouse. Jack rings the
bell. Moments later it is opened by a young
trendy bearded guy, CORDELL INNES-BROWN.

                    CORDELL
              (Well spoken)
        Greetings.

                    JACK
        Cordell Innes-Brown?

                    CORDELL
        For my sins... Mr Scanlon I
        presume?

                    JACK
Yes, and one of my colleagues
Krzysztof Jurczak.

                    CORDELL
        (Offering hand)
Come in and be welcome.
And please call me Cordell.

INT. TOWN HOUSE. LONDON. NIGHT.

Jack and Krzys are standing around a computer
screen with Cordell and two of his colleagues.
A young, attractive (20 something) woman,
CHARLIE QUAIFE and Anglo/Chinese nerd FINLAY
TONG, who is also in his late 20s.

                    CORDELL
How did you hear about us?

                    JACK
My daughter watches your
YouTube channel.

                    CORDELL
Cool... Anyway, may I
introduce you to two of my
colleagues. Finlay Tong...

                    FINLAY
               (Well spoken)
          Hi... I believe.

                    CORDELL
          And Charlie Quaife.

                    CHARLIE
               (Well-spoken)
          Hi... And I don't.

                    JACK
          Charlie?

                    CHARLIE
          A preferable alternative
          to Charlotte, which I
          absolutely detest.

                    CORDELL
          Whatever you do don't call
          her Charlotte, or there will
          be hell to pay.

                    JACK
          Fair enough.

                    KRZYS
          Nice to meet.

                    CORDELL
Charlie complements Finlay
and I by looking at things
from a scientific perspective.

                    CHARLIE
And proving it's mostly
all bollocks.

                    FINLAY
Some of the time.

                    CHARLIE
Most of the time.

                    CORDELL
Let's just say she keeps
our feet on the ground.
        (Beat)
Anyway, you said you have
something interesting to
show us.

Jack removes a memory stick from his
coat pocket.

                    JACK
I managed to download a copy
before our employers censored
it.

                  CORDELL
Cool.

                    JACK
We were told not to discuss
it with anyone.

                  FINLAY
Why not?

                    JACK
I don't know. They accepted
responsibility for our
colleagues accident, provided
we all agreed never to
discuss with anyone what
really happened.

                  CHARLIE
So why have you come to us?

                    JACK
There's something weird going
on in that place and we want
to know what.

                  CORDELL
But surely your employers
want to get to the bottom of
this as much as anyone.

                    JACK
You'd think so but maybe
it's easier, and cheaper,
to sweep it under the carpet.

                  CHARLIE
Or maybe they simply don't
think it's interesting
enough.

                   KRZYS
Play stick. Judge yourself.

Cordell inserts the stick into his laptop
and opens file. (The contents are a mixture
of camera stills and camcorder.)

                    JACK
        That's the first one.

They look at the footage. Above Dion's
shoulder is a small translucent sphere (orb)

                    JACK (Cont'd)
        It wasn't there when I
        took it.

Cordell and Finlay look with some interest.
The next shot is far more intriguing. It is
footage taken of Dion next to station sign.
A few more spheres have formed around him..

                    CORDELL.
        Interesting.

                    CHARLIE
        Wow, specs of dust caught in
        the light.

                    FINLAY
        Looks like orbs to me.

The orbs then merge to form a translucent dark mist that swirls around Dion before vanishing.

> CHARLIE
> I stand corrected. Specs of dust and a bit of mist caught in the light.

> FINLAY
> Wow, look at the mist. It seems to be controlled.

> CHARLIE
> Yeah, by an air current.

> FINLAY
> Mist moved by air does not move around like that. This is very intriguing.

> CORDELL
> I agree, this is very cool.

Next. Camera footage Krzys took in the tunnel just before Marty leaps out at him.

> KRZYS
> Look at this one.

The footage has captured Marty's grinning face, However, behind him, over his left shoulder the same dark mist is seen. This time it appears to morph into a 'loose' spiritual human form hovering above him.

                    JACK
          Keep watching.

                    FINLAY
          Oh WOW! Awesome...

                    CORDELL
          That is awesome!

Charlie rolls her eyes.

                    CORDELL (Cont'd)
          Oh come on Charlie even
          you have to admit that is
          pretty interesting.

                    CHARLIE
    So it happens look a bit
    like, what is commonly
    perceived to be, a spiritual
    manifestation... But that
    doesn't mean that it is one
    does it?

                     JACK
    We're not saying that it is.
    But you got to admit, given
    the history of the place
    and what happened to our
    colleague there's something
    pretty strange going on.

                    CORDELL
    Absolutely.

                    FINLAY
    Totally.

Digestive pause.

                    CORDELL
    So when can you get us in
    there?

INT. MINI BUS. LONDON. NIGHT.

Waiting inside the Mini bus, are Cordell, Charlie and Finlay. With them is a plump, eccentric looking, 50 something Afro-Caribbean woman, LAYLA LAWLER, who, with her short dyed blonde hairstyle, appears much younger than her age.

                    FINLAY
               (To Layla)
          So what part of the U.S.A
          are you from?

                    LAYLA
          Calgary. Alberta.

                    FINLAY
          Is that near Texas?

                    LAYLA
          It's in Canada.

                    FINLAY
          Oh. Forgive me.
          Geography isn't one of my
          strong points.

                    CHARLIE
          We'd never have guessed.

Awkward pause.

                    FINLAY
          So you're Canadian then?

                    LAYLA
          People from Canada usually are.

Charlie is amused.

                    FINLAY
          Yes of course... It's just
          that, correct me if I'm
          wrong, I detect something
          else in your accent.

                    CORDELL
          Layla's originally from
          Montserrat.

                    FINLAY
          Africa?

                    CORDELL
          Close. It's an island in
          the Caribbean.

                    FINLAY
          Oh...

                    LAYLA
          Parents emigrated when I
          was nine... Been shivering
          ever since.

EXT. UNDERGROUND STATION. NIGHT.

Jack unlocks a huge padlock and removes
a thick chain that is securing the metal
shutters that cover the station entrance.

He then unlocks the entrance door and steps
in. Once inside he beckons Cordell and his
team, including Krzys and Dion, who are
waiting in a van.

INT. UNDERGROUND STATION. PASSAGEWAYS.

Cordell, Finlay and Charlie are joined by two others from their team, SEAN and MARINA, who provide technical support. As they descend the deep spiral staircase and enter the tunnel passageways that lead down to the platform, each of them are enthralled as their torch beams light up the way, revealing adverts and posters from a bygone era.

INT. PASSAGEWAY. FURTHER ON.

As the group near the end of the passageway, they discover that there has been additional collapse of the entrance masonry which is partially blocking access to the platform.

> CORDELL
> (To Jack)
> I thought you said everything
> is safe?

> JACK
> This must have only just
> happened. It wasn't as bad
> last time we were here.

INT. PLATFORM.

Once into the platform area, again their torches illuminate the pitch black. Ad-lib remarks. As the other members of the team express great interest Layla looks enthralled as if she is tuning into something.

> LAYLA
>> Oh my Lord!...
>>> (Beat)
>> Oh my sweet Jesus!

> CORDELL
>> What is it?

> LAYLA
>> WOW!... This place is unreal!... There is <u>SO</u> much energy.
>>> (Beat)
>> I am feeling this so strong.

Layla closes her eyes and focuses.

                    LAYLA (Cont'd)
Dozens and dozens.
         (Beat)
Many strong presences - far
too strong to be visitations.
         (Pause)
Two of them especially. They
are definitely resident.

                 CORDELL
Cool.

                 FINLAY
Awesome.

                  DION
I don't know about you
but I sense fuck all.

                 CHARLIE
Me neither.

                  KRZYS
Maybe you not sense but
I do. Something here...
I feel.

LATER.

> LAYLA
>
> How old is this place?

> CORDELL
>
> Marina.

> MARINA
>
> One hundred and thirty nine
> years. The station was opened
> on January sixteenth,
> eighteen eighty three, as
> part of the Metropolitan
> line.
> > (Beat)
> It was closed for five years
> during world war two when
> it was principally used as
> a bomb shelter, hospital
> and mortuary.
> > (Beat)
> More interestingly the
> station has had a long
> history of unexplained
> fatalities and suicides.
> Fifty three in total - fifty
> two of which have been men.

                    MARINA (Cont'd)
These deaths led to the
closure of the station in
nineteen fifty two...
          (Beat)
Of course that wasn't the
official reason.

                    CORDELL
What was?

                    MARINA
Apparently a huge investment
was needed to bring the
station up to date but the
passenger numbers didn't
justify the expense.

                    LAYLA
So what about these
unexplained fatalities.
Did anyone ever investigate?

                    MARINA
If they did the findings were
never made public.

                    MARINA (Cont'd)
However, and this is the
really interesting bit, over
many decades, dozens of
Underground staff and members
of the public have reported
seeing the apparitions of two
women, both dressed in late
nineteenth century period
clothing. One of which seems
to manifest just before or
after a fatal incident.

                    FINLAY
Wow! Does anyone have
any idea who these women
might be?

                    MARINA
Well, the entity who has
been seen around the time
of the incidents is thought
to be that of a well-known
actress called...

                    LAYLA
Edith Sybil Rattray.

                    MARINA
        Edith Rattray — wow, how
        did you know?.

They all look impressed. Ad-lib remarks.
Wow, no way, etc.

                    LAYLA
        I'm psychic. Dead folk tell
        me stuff.

                    DION
        Any chance of this weeks
        lottery numbers?...

                    MARINA
        Edith Rattray was a well known
        stage actress and socialite
        who performed at the Royal
        Piccadilly theatre that used to
        be across the street from here.

Marina holds up a copy of a portrait
photograph of Edith taken during her heyday.

                    MARINA (Cont'd)
        Here is a picture of her
        taken during the peak of
        her fame.

                    MARINA (Cont'd)
          Unfortunately, a couple of
          years after this picture
          was taken, she took her
          own life after brutally
          murdering her fiancé in a fit
          of jealous rage.

                    LAYLA
          Threw herself in front of a
          train from this very spot
          didn't she?

                    MARINA
          She did.

Again the others look suitably enthralled —
with the exception of Charlie.

                    FINLAY
          Wow! That is awesome.

                    LAYLA
          There are no secrets in
          the spirit world.

                    CORDELL
              (After pause)
         Cool... What about the other
         woman. Did you uncover
         anything about her — who she
         is, was, etc?

                    MARINA
         Nothing, She remains a
         total mystery.

Moments later Layla appears flushed. She
buries her head in her hands and starts to
breathe deeply. She then looks towards the
west tunnel.

                    CORDELL
         Layla. What is it?

                    LAYLA
         I'm getting a vibe...
              (Beat)
         Something is coming.
              (Beat)
         Towards us from the tunnel.

                    CHARLIE
          That was quick.

Unexpectedly, there is a bright flash as one
of the camera motion sensors is triggered.
They all look. Layla then begins to turn
strangely trance like — but not dramatic
or false.

                    CORDELL
          What's coming! What's
          coming? Quick lights off,
          cameras on!

                    FINLAY
          Awesome...

                    CORDELL
          Focus on the tunnel.

All goes deathly silent as they fixate on
Layla who in turn is watching something
at the mouth of the west tunnel. One of
the lights closest to the tunnel entrance
flickers briefly — then another one which is
closer.

                    LAYLA
          It's stopped.

                    CORDELL
               (To Sean)
          Any reading on the EMF?

Close up of EMF detector in Sean's hand.
The needle is bouncing.

                    SEAN
          I'm getting a strong
          reading. There wasn't one
          a second ago.

                    KRZYS
               (To Sean)
          What it do?

                    SEAN
          It's an EMF detector. It
          detects the presence of
          electromagnetic fields.
          A sign of paranormal activity.

                    LAYLA
          Sshhhhhh!
               (Concentrates)
          Do not be a afraid — do not
          be shy, please come forward.

                    LAYLA (Cont'd)
          We only wish to communicate.
          We wish you no harm.

                    FINLAY
          Is it trying to communicate?

                    LAYLA
          Sshhhhh!
                    (Few beats)
          If you understand me, can you
          please give us some sort of
          sign? A noise perhaps.

After a short pause a faint metallic tap is
heard as if an object has made contact with
one of the rail tracks.

                    KRZYS
          What was that?

                    JACK
          Thought I heard something.

                    LAYLA
          Shhhhhhh!... If that was you
          could you do it again, a
          little louder this time?

Slight pause, then the tap is heard again, slightly louder.

                    LAYLA
          Can you do it again, this
          time with two taps?

Two loud distinctive taps are heard — much to everyone's delight.

                    JACK
          Jesus do you hear that?

                    CHARLIE
          Probably a rat.

                    JACK
          Clever rat.

                    LAYLA
          SShhhhh!
               (Pause)
          I would like to ask you
          something. Could you tap once
          for no, and twice for yes?

After a couple of beats two loud taps are heard. The group are fascinated.

> LAYLA (Cont'd)
> Can I ask why you have not
> gone towards the light. Is
> there something keeping
> you here?

After a pause, two distinctive taps
are heard.

> LAYLA (Cont'd)
> Is it because you cannot find
> the light?

After a pause, a distinctive tap.

> LAYLA (Cont'd)
> Then is it because of
> unfinished business?

After a pause, two loud taps. Suddenly the
group is distracted by a strong gust of air
that comes belching out of the east tunnel
— setting off the motion detectors.

> FINLAY
> What on earth was that?

> CHARLIE
> Eh... Air current.

                    FINLAY
That was no normal air
current.

                    CORDELL
            (Moments later)
Layla, can you ask this
spirit if it can reveal
itself?

                    LAYLA
Not really.

                    CORDELL
Why not?

                    LAYLA
Because it's gone.

                    CORDELL
Where did it go?

                    LAYLA
Back from where ever it
came from.

> CHARLIE
> (After beat)
> Another camera shy spook.
> What a surprise.

LATER.

Shots of team setting up equipment in
strategic places. Motion detectors and fixed
cameras, etc.

> CORDELL
> Ok, we'll split into three
> groups. Team A, Jack you,
> Krzys and Dion. Team B,
> Layla, Marina and Myself and
> C, Charlie, Fin and Sean.

> JACK
> I think it would be a lot
> safer if one of us engineers
> was present in each group.

                    CORDELL
Fair enough. Ok. How about
Dion, you join Charlie and
Fin. Krzys, you join with
Sean and Marina, and Jack you
come with Layla and myself.

                    JACK
Okay.

                    CORDELL
Cool... Right, I suggest
that team A check out the
east facing tunnel, B
stays here and monitors the
platform area and C team does
the west facing tunnel.

                    LAYLA
Cordell I ain't staying here.
That spirit came from the
west tunnel. So that's where
I'm going.

                    CORDELL
Eh, okay - change of plan...

LATER. WEST TUNNEL.

Cordell's group gingerly inch their way through the west tunnel. Jack's torch beam illuminates dozens of ball like reflections followed by mass scurrying.

A bit further Layla stops.

> LAYLA
> I feel it...

> CORDELL
> What?

> LAYLA
> The entity who came to us...
> I am feeling it stronger.

> JACK
> Why is it so shy?

> LAYLA
> Not sure. But I sense it
> might be hiding from
> something.

> CORDELL
> From what?

> LAYLA

I don't know.

EAST TUNNEL.

Finlay's group tread even more gingerly. Especially Finlay who has the camcorder.

> CHARLIE

Come on Finlay keep up.

> FINLAY

Are you sure these rails are no longer live?

> DION

I don't know, they might be.

> FINLAY

What?! What do you mean they might be!

> DION

Do you really think I would be walking on them if they were.

> FINLAY

Couldn't you just say that.

Dion catches Charlie's eye. They share a
devilish grin.

FURTHER ON.

                    CHARLIE
          Is it me or has it just
          become a lot colder all
          of a sudden.

                    FINLAY
          A lot colder.

Charlie takes a reading from the
IR thermometer.

                    CHARLIE
          According to this the
          temperature has shot down.

                    DION
          That's not unusual down here.
          You get different air currents
          drifting through. Warm air,
          cold.

Suddenly hundreds of small beads of light
are reflected in Dion's torch beam.

                    FINLAY
        Oh my God, Oh God! What is
        that?.. What is it!?

The   shiny   lights   then   disperse   in   a
mad scurry.

                    DION
        Rats. Dozens of them.

                    FINLAY
        Had me going there for
        a minute.

                    CHARLIE
        You know Finlay, for someone
        who does this job, you really
        are a bloody great wuss.

                    FINLAY
        Me, a wuss? Don't be
        ridiculous.

Moments later.

                    FINLAY (Cont'd)
        Argh! Argh! Argh!

                    CHARLIE
          Jesus, what now!?

                    FINLAY
          My face. Something
          scratched it!

Charlie sighs with exasperation. Dion
shines his torch onto Finlay illuminating
his face.

                    DION
          It's bleeding. How did you
          do that?

                    FINLAY
          I don't know, it just
          happened.

                    CHARLIE
          What do you mean, it just
          happened?

                    FINLAY
          Like, it just happened...
          I don't bloody know!

                    CHARLIE
        Did you walk into something?
        A dangling cable perhaps.

                    FINLAY
        No! I didn't walk into
        anything.
              (Beat)
        God, you don't think it was
        one of those rats do you?

                    DION
        A rat? I don't think so.

                    FINLAY
        How do you know, anything
        could happen down here.
        They could have genetically
        mutated into...

                    CHARLIE
              (Interrupts)
        Into what!? A strain of
        man eating, blood sucking,
        vampire zombie rats.

Dion sniggers.

                    FINLAY
          I was going to say, a strain
          that has lost its fear of man
          and is not afraid to attack.

                    CHARLIE
          Now who's being ridiculous.

                    FINLAY
          It's true. I saw it on the
          Discovery channel.

Pause. Dion notices a diode flickering on the
EMF detector that he is holding. He shows it
to Fin and Charlie.

                    DION
          Eh, the lights on this
          machine are flickering. Does
          that mean anything?

Charlie and Finlay look at the EMF.

                    FINLAY
          Wow, what's causing that?

                    DION
          What does it mean?

                    FINLAY
          We are close to an
          Electromagnetic field.
          A sign of paranormal
          activity.

                    CHARLIE
          Or a source of electricity.
          As in wiring and cables.

                    FINLAY
          But the cables aren't live
          in this section - are they?

Close up of meter. The diode lights are
indicating a very strong field up ahead.

                    FINLAY (Cont'd)
          Wow, it seems to be getting
          stronger and stronger.

Dion's attention is drawn to the tracks.
He listens.

                    DION
          Hold it a second.

                    FINLAY
          What?

                    DION
        Shhh, quiet...
              (Listens further)
        What was that?

                    FINLAY
        What was what?

Dion shines his torch onto one of the rail
tracks - which is beginning to vibrate.

                    DION
        That! Listen...

The vibration becomes more pronounced...
then stronger — then...

                    DION (Cont'd)
        No, no it can't be!

                    CHARLIE
        What is it!?

Dion looks towards the direction of the
vibration and sees something shocking. Two
white lights piercing through the pitch
black like a pair of ethereal eyes.

As it gets closer the vibration gets stronger accompanied by an eerie rumble and neon electric flashes. The trio stand transfixed.

                    DION
          IT'S A FUCKING TRAIN!!

                    FINLAY
          A train... But?

                    DION
          RUN!! RUN!!

With the approaching rumble rapidly developing into a cacophony of clatters and screeches, the horrified trio run for their lives back through the pitch black with only their torches to see.

In utter panic they each stumble their way over sleepers and dimly illuminated track obstacles as the train thunders closer and closer.

(At no point do we see a physical train. Just light and sound)

PLATFORM.

Krzysztof is sitting at the edge of the platform when he hears screaming and shouting from the east tunnel.

                    KRZYS
          Listen, you hear?

                    SEAN
          Sounds like shouting.

                    MARINA
          What the!...

Krzys, Sean and Marina dash over to the tunnel entrance just as frantic Dion and Charlie appear, screaming "TRAIN!!"

With the thundering train only a few meters behind, Dion deftly leaps up onto the platform. Once on he immediately turns to assist Charlie who is right behind him. However, Krzys is right there and yanks her to safety.

                    MARINA
          Where's Finlay!?

They all yell 'FINLAY!!'

With the deafening sound of the train dangerously close behind, Finlay is only a few yards from the safety of the platform. He then trips and screams helplessly as the train passes over him.

On the platform, the remaining crew look on with shock and awe as they expect a train to come crashing out of the tunnel. But to their surprise, the only thing that belts out is a powerful blast of ice cold wind that almost sweeps them off their feet and temporarily cuts all power.

30 seconds later the power is restored and the battery lanterns flicker back on. They hear a groaning sound from the tunnel and Finlay, clearly in shock, staggers out.

WEST TUNNEL.

Cordell, Layla and Jack are slowly edging their way through the west tunnel.

>   LAYLA
>   This place is a minefield of
>   energy. It is so strong.

>   CORDELL
>   Cool... Any sign of the
>   entity we encountered before?

>   LAYLA
>   Yes, I can feel it. And it's
>   presence is getting stronger.

>   CORDELL
>   Awesome.

Suddenly Cordell's walkie talkie crackles loudly followed by Sean's voice.

>   SEAN (Over W/T)
>   Cordell, Cordell! Come in!

>   CORDELL
>   (Into W/T)
>   Sean — Cordell... over.

                    SEAN (Over W/T)
          Cordell, you'll never believe
          what just happened. You've got
          to get back here... over.

                    CORDELL
          Sean - Why, what's happened?

The signal breaks up.

                    CORDELL (Cont'd)
          Sean... Sean, are you there?

The Walkie talkie hisses and crackles.

                    CORDELL (Cont'd)
          Bugger.

                    JACK
          What was that about?

                    CORDELL
          I don't know. But whatever it
          was it sounded quite exiting.

                    LAYLA
          You two go back if you want
          but I am carrying on this a
          way.

Their attention is suddenly drawn to a vibration running through the railway tracks. It becomes more pronounced.

> JACK
> Strange.

> CORDELL
> What?
> (Beat. Listens)
> What is that?

> JACK
> Eh, a vibration...

> CORDELL
> What sort of vibration?

> JACK
> The sort that an approaching train makes.

> CORDELL
> Really.

Vibration gets louder.

> CORDELL (Cont'd)
> But that's impossible, right?

                    JACK
          Absolutely, there's no way.

We hear a faint distant rumble.

                    CORDELL
          You're really sure about
          that?

                    JACK
          Of course. No train has run
          on these tracks in over
          seventy years!

Looking down the tunnel towards the east,
a pair of white lights suddenly appear
accompanied by a rumble and clatter.

                    JACK (Cont'd)
          You have got to be
          kidding me!
               (Beat)
          FOR FUCK SAKE RUN!... NOW!!
          FOLLOW ME!

As the approaching rumble gives way to a loud metallic squeal and clatter, a panicked Jack runs further into the tunnel, with Cordell close behind. (Again no physical train, just light and sound)

> JACK (Cont'd)
> THERE'S A RECESS, JUST
> UP AHEAD!!

Cordell looks behind, to his great surprise Layla isn't running with them. He stops.

> CORDELL
> LAYLA!! LAYLA! What are
> you doing!?

Layla is still standing in the same spot, facing the oncoming train.

> JACK
> COME ON!!

> CORDELL
> LAYLA!!

> JACK
> What the fuck is she doing!
> LAYLA!!

Still standing, Layla slowly turns half her body towards Jack and Cordell and smiles knowingly.

                    LAYLA
          You can run if you want to...
          But I'm staying put.

Jack and Cordell look at her in utter disbelief, then run a few yards until Jack's torch beam illuminates a small recess in the tunnel wall.

                    JACK
          Quick in here!

Both take cover in the recess then look back in horror at Layla as the train thunders towards her. She however, remains calm and steadfast. Moments before impact she focuses hard and closes her eyes...

Then just as the train is set to mow her down it unexpectedly dematerialises and all that hits her is a moderate force of icy wind.

Jack and Cordell can't believe it and immediately go to her. Ad-lib remarks, etc.

                    CORDELL
          Jesus are you alright!?

                    LAYLA
          Now that's what I call
          energy!

                    JACK
          What the fuck was it!?

                    LAYLA
          A warning.

                    JACK
          A warning? A warning
          from who?

                    LAYLA
          I don't know. But whoever it
          is sure doesn't want us here.

                    CORDELL
          Awesome! Absolutely awesome!

PLATFORM.

Back on the platform, with the others watching, Finlay is reviewing footage on a lap top that he took earlier in the east tunnel, just before he was scratched.

Dion and Charlie can be heard talking in the playback. As the camera pans a faint shadowy figure appears and stares momentarily before disappearing. Intrigued, Finley rewinds and repeats play back. Again the apparition appears on screen.

Ad-lib group reaction.

> FINLAY
> WOW! Who or what is that? I
> never saw anyone in there!
> This could well be a
> spiritual entity and we have
> it on camera!

> CHARLIE
> Hold on. We don't know what
> it is.

> FINLAY
> Oh, here we go.

                    CHARLIE
It could be a homeless person
for all we know.

                    FINLAY
What the hell would a
homeless person be doing
down here?

                    CHARLIE
Because they're homeless.

                    FINLAY
Eh, so why didn't we see or
hear anyone then?

                    CHARLIE
I don't know. Maybe they
didn't want us to see them.
Anyone caught living down
here would be kicked out,
fined or even jailed.

                    FINLAY
What about the train
phenomena. You going to say
that you didn't see or hear
that as well?

                    DION
        That was well weird.

                    CHARLIE
        We saw and heard something
        yes. But maybe it was
        some sort of naturally
        occurring phenomena.

                    FINLAY
        Really! Like what?

                    CHARLIE
        These old tunnels are very
        close to parts of the network
        that are in constant use
        today. Is it possible that
        what we experienced was the
        sound of a nearby train,
        amplified by the acoustics of
        the tunnel itself?

The others dismiss Charlie's suggestion —
specially Finlay.

                    DION
        Maybe. But if that's the
        case how come we don't hear
        it all the time?

                        KRZYS
            Why all talking. Finlay make
            record on camera, let us see
            playback and make judgement.

All agree.

Finlay fast forwards video to point where
Dion notices rail line vibration. (P68) The
sound of an approaching train can clearly
be heard just before Dion shouts RUN!

From then on the footage is shaky and blurred
as Finlay scrambles for his life. His heavy
breathing and panicked shrieks mask most of
all other sounds.

                        FINLAY
            Shit...

Groans of disappointment from others.

WEST TUNNEL.

Deeper into the west tunnel, Cordell still can't get the radio to work.

>   CORDELL
>   Still nothing.

>   LAYLA
>   There's still a lot of energy
>   about. It's most likely
>   messing with the signal.

>   JACK
>   Perhaps we should turn
>   back. See what happened to
>   the others.

>   LAYLA
>   Shhhh... Hold it.

A little further on the tunnel splits into a left fork and a right.

>   CORDELL
>   What now?

                    JACK
        If my memory serves me right
        this fork leads to a siding.

                    LAYLA
        Good. That's where she is.

                    CORDELL
        she?

                    LAYLA
        I can sense a female.

                    CORDELL
        Cool... Is it Edith?

                    LAYLA
        I don't think it is.

The trio tentatively walk further on into
the left fork tunnel.

FURTHER ON.

One of the torch beams illuminates something large up ahead.

> CORDELL
> What is that?

> JACK
> It's an old train.

As they get closer they find an old train (two carriages) that looks as if it has been abandoned and forgotten for a very long time. With helmet torch beams illuminating the dilapidated rolling stock, Cordell and Jack climb up to look inside.

> CORDELL
> Oh WOW! This is just awesome. Look at it.

> JACK
> It must have been here at least fifty years.

Moments later.

> LAYLA
> Hold it! Shhhh! Quiet.
> We have a visitor.

Layla squeezes her way along the tight gap between the train and the tunnel wall. Jack and Cordell gingerly get down from the carriage and quietly follow.

> LAYLA (Cont'd)
> Hello...
>> (Beat)
> Hello...

At the front of the train Layla finds herself at a dead-end. The train is parked at a set of buffers that sit just in front of a old brick wall at the end of the line.

> LAYLA (Cont'd)
>> (To wall)
> Yes, I can see you. Can you tell me your name?
>> (Beat)
> Hello Mary. My name is Layla.
>> (Beat)
> Mary please calm yourself.
> We mean you no harm and wish only to help.

                    LAYLA (Cont'd)
                (Couple of beats)
         Of course I will help you.
         But first I need to understand
         what is keeping you here.
         Why haven't you gone towards
         the light?

                    CORDELL
         Who are you talking to?

                    LAYLA
         Shhhh!
                (Pause)
         These are my companions.
         They will help you too.

Cordell starts shooting video again.

                    CORDELL
         I've got orbs! I've got orbs!

                    LAYLA
         Mary, why haven't you gone
         towards the light?
                (Pause)
         But why not? What is stopping
         you?... Please tell me
         what happened?

INT. ROYAL PICADILLY THEATRE. LONDON. DAY. 1882.

On stage, a small ensemble of actors take a bow in front of a very appreciative audience gathered from London's high society.

One of them, EDITH RATTRAY (Mid 30s), who is standing in the centre, steps forward and is greeted with a loud cheer and more adulation.

WINGS/STAGE.

Watching in the wings is a immaculately dressed, distinguished, albeit pompous looking gentleman, RANDOLPH MORTON (Mid 40s) who is obviously delighted with the audience reaction.

> RANDOLPH
> BRAVO!... BRAVO!

After a few moments he joins the cast on stage. To great applause and cheers, Randolph bows and waves. He then embraces Edith and kisses her full on the lips. Hand in hand the pair then take another bow.

BACKSTAGE.

As Randolph and Edith make their way arm in arm to the greenroom, they are congratulated by a throng of theatre employees. Most of whom address them as Sir or Ma'm.

Among them is a pretty young woman in her mid twenties, MARY ELWES.

> MARY
> (West country)
> Congratulations Mr Morton.

> RANDOLPH
> Thank you Mary.

> MARY
> Congratulations Madam.

Edith ignores Mary.

> EDITH
> Who is she?

> RANDOLPH
> Eh, works in wardrobe
> I think.

                    EDITH
      You think? You managed to
      recall her name.

                  RANDOLPH
      A lot of girls work for me
      dear. Some names I recall,
      some I do not.

                    EDITH
      Only the pretty ones it seems.

                  RANDOLPH
      Not one more beautiful or
      more talented than you though
      my darling.

EXT. STREET. LONDON. NIGHT. 1882.

Mary is standing waiting on a street corner.
She has a scarf covering her head. Moments
later a shiny black (closed) horse drawn
carriage pulls up across the road. Mary
crosses the road towards the carriage.
EMERSON, the coach driver, opens the door
for her and she steps up and in.

INT. CARRIAGE. LONDON. NIGHT. 1882.

Randolph Morton is already seated puffing a large cigar. Mary enters and Emerson closes the door.

> RANDOLPH
>
> Ah, Mary my dear. Apologies for all the cloak and dagger but a man of my station cannot be too careful.
>> (Beat)
> Now, what seems to be the problem?

> MARY
>
> There's no easy way of saying it.

> RANDOLPH
>
> Well spit it out girl I haven't got all evening.

> MARY
>> (After beat)
> I'm with child.

                    RANDOLPH
Oh... I see. And you are
telling me this why exactly?

                      MARY
Why do you think?

                    RANDOLPH
No, no there must be
some mistake!

                      MARY
There is no mistake.

                    RANDOLPH
But how can you be so sure?
You are a pretty girl - you
must have many male admirers!

                      MARY
You are the only one that
I... you know.

                    RANDOLPH
Oh my Lord. This is
impossible! Simply
impossible!

                    MARY
I'm sorry but I had to
tell you.

                    RANDOLPH
For heaven's sake!

                    MARY
I don't know what else to do.

                    RANDOLPH
I am getting married in three
months. Have you any idea
what this means. If any of
this gets out my reputation
will be ruined!
        (Beat)
Who else knows of this!?

                    MARY
No one. So help me god I
swear it.

                    RANDOLPH
Are you absolutely positive?

                    MARY
Absolutely, yes.

                    RANDOLPH
          That's something at least.
                    (Pause)
          Alright here's what to do.
          There's a woman in
          Whitechapel. She's very clean
          and very thorough.

                    MARY
          A woman?

                    RANDOLPH
          Don't worry - I'll see to it.
          It won't cost you a penny.

                    MARY
          What woman?

                    RANDOLPH
          The sort of woman that makes
          unwanted problems, such as
          yours, go away.

The penny drops, Mary is appalled.

                    RANDOLPH (Cont'd)
          Well you're surely not
          thinking of keeping the
          damn thing?

                    MARY
Of course I am!

                  RANDOLPH
What! Have you completely
lost your senses.

                    MARY
You presume that I would be
so heartless as to take the
life of an innocent unborn,
yet you suggest that I have
lost my senses. You're the
father for heaven's sake!

                  RANDOLPH
So you claim.

                    MARY
I am telling the truth, I
swear it.

                    RANDOLPH
              (After beat)
         Listen closely and heed this
         most carefully. If you choose
         to decline my very reasonable
         offer and persist on a more
         ethical, if not wise, course
         of action that is entirely up
         to you.
              (Beat)
         However, should you ever
         contact me again or utter
         anything of this matter to
         another living soul, I will
         make life for you, and the
         bastard you are carrying,
         very difficult indeed...
         Do I make myself clear?!

EXT. CARRIAGE. STREET. LONDON. NIGHT. 1882.

Outside the carriage, coach driver Emerson
is listening to the conversation inside.
Suddenly the carriage door bursts open and
he quickly jumps out of earshot.

A distraught Mary then alights the carriage
and runs off into the night.

INT. OFFICE. THEATRE. LONDON. DAY. 1882.

Dressed in a manner befitting her status, Edith
Rattray opens a door and wafts arrogantly
into an office. Sitting behind a desk is
secretary MISS HEWITT. With contemptuous
silence, Edith breezes straight past and
makes her way to another door.

                    MISS HEWITT
          Eh, excuse me Ma'm. Mr Morton
          is conducting business at
          the moment.

                    EDITH
          Very soon I will be Mrs
          Randolph Morton. Whatever
          is his business will be
          my business.

Just as Edith makes a grab for the door
handle the door unexpectedly opens,
revealing Randolph and two menacing looking
gentlemen. MR STALKER and MR JANUS.

                    RANDOLPH
          Ah, Edith darling. A little
          early aren't we.

                    EDITH
          Is that a problem dear?

                  RANDOLPH
          Eh, no of course not. These
          Gentlemen were just leaving.

The two men are fairly well dressed but are
obviously not proper Gentlemen. As the pair
walk out they give Edith a look which makes
her feel slightly ill at ease.

                  MR STALKER
                    (Cockney)
          We'll be in touch then.

                  RANDOLPH
          Thank you Mr Stalker. Mr
          Janus. Good day.

Just as they leave Stalker and Janus tip
their hats in a half hearted gesture of
respect.

                  MR STALKER
          Madam.

Mr Janus remains silent. Edith manages a
cursory nod. The pair then exit.

                    EDITH
Who the devil are they?

                  RANDOLPH
Two men I employ
occasionally.

                    EDITH
To do what may I ask?

                  RANDOLPH
Nothing you need worry
about dear.

                    EDITH
I am not a child Randolph.

                  RANDOLPH
Eh, collection of outstanding
debts, that sort of thing.
They are very persuasive.

                    EDITH
I can imagine. And how
ever did you come to meet
their acquaintance?

                  RANDOLPH
Emerson introduced me.

                    EDITH
        Emerson... Your driver?

                    RANDOLPH
        I believe he and Mr Janus
        are related.
                (Beat, beat)
        Now, shall we go to dinner.

EXT. STREET. EAST LONDON. NIGHT. 1882.

Mary is walking home alone in a dimly lit
street in London's East End. As she passes
a dark alleyway she is grabbed from behind
by two masked assailants, pulled into the
shadows and bashed on the head with a cosh.

INT. UNDERGROUND TUNNEL CONSTRUCTION SITE. LONDON. 1882.

In a dark claustrophobic underground tunnel, dimly lit by a half dozen or so gas lanterns, three shadowy figures struggle to find their way in the gloom. The tunnel is still under construction. The floor is made up of thick wood planking, thick iron ribs form the tubular shape and the rails have yet to be laid.

The first figure, that of a thin and dirty looking NIGHT-WATCHMAN, holds up a hand held lantern as he leads the way.

The dim light reveals the other two men as Stalker and Janus, who are carrying between them what appears to be a motionless human body encased in a large cloth sack.

> MR JANUS
> How much further? My back is killing me!

> NIGHT-WATCHMAN
> Not far now. We're almost there.

A BIT FURTHER.

The night-watchman's lantern illuminates a half built brick wall. (Same one as on page 86) The wall, which at the moment is no more than five feet high, is intended to cap off a solid earth dead end.

> NIGHT-WATCHMAN
> This is it.

> MR STALKER
> Thank fuck for that.

Stalker and Janus put the motionless body down. The night-watchman then shows them the cavity behind the half built wall and the solid earth.

> NIGHT-WATCHMAN
> In a couple hours the early
> shift will finish bricking up.
> Bung the stiff behind the wall
> and it's well hid for good.

All of a sudden the motionless body moves and starts to groan.

Hysterical screaming follows, startling the two thugs and frightening the crap out of the night-watchman. (Ad-lib reaction)

> MR STALKER
> I thought she was a gonner!?

> MR JANUS
> Thought so too. Bashed her
> hard enough.

Mr Janus looks about and spots a shovel leaning against the wall. He grabs it and uses it to deliver a swift fatal blow to the head of the writhing victim, who instantly falls silent.

> MR JANUS (Cont'd)
> Happy now.

The night-watchman is clearly shaken.

> NIGHT-WATCHMAN
> That sounded like a woman
> that did. You never said it
> was a woman.

> MR STALKER
> What of it?

                    NIGHT-WATCHMAN
          Bad luck to kill a woman.

                    MR STALKER
          Only if you blab about it. So
          unless you want to join her,
          I suggest you shut your trap
          and keep it that way.

The night-Watchmen immediately does as he
is told.

LATER.

Stalker and Janus lift the body up over
the wall and let it fall down the other
side. It is now trapped in the narrow space
between the unfinished brick wall and the
solid earth.

                    MR STALKER
          Let's get out of here...
          Place gives me the creeps.

HOURS LATER.

Construction workers are busy in the tunnel working amidst a cacophony of thumping, banging and drilling. The bricklayers have almost finished the end cap wall.

A shaft of light from the other side of the unfinished wall partially illuminates the narrow cavity space where Mary's body lies motionless. Moments later we hear muffled groans as she gradually regains consciousness. Mary wriggles out of the sack revealing her bloodied and bewildered.

Upon realizing her impending fate Mary struggles to her feet.

Infused with sheer terror she screams repeatedly with every ounce of strength she has.

However, due to the noise of the construction on the other side of the wall, her screams go unnoticed.

Mary can only watch helplessly as the final few bricks are cemented in place, diminishing further what little is left of the remaining light.

A small shaft of light illuminates Mary's terror struck eyes. As the last brick is added the shaft of light dies leaving her trapped and alone in the cold pitch black...

Agonised scream!

SAME LOCATION. PRESENT DAY.

Layla's tone is different. She is visibly shocked and distressed. Jack and Cordell also look shaken. Ad-lib comments.

                    CORDELL
          It's like something out of a
          gothic horror story. I can't
          imagine what she must have
          gone through.

                    JACK
          None of us can... That's if
          it's true.

                    LAYLA

Of course it is. Why would she
lie about such a thing...
We got to get her the hell out
of there as soon as we can.

                    CORDELL

Totally. We got to report
this right away.

                    JACK

Hold on a minute. Report it
to who? We're not supposed
to be here remember. If my
bosses found out you lot are
down here without consent
there's a very strong chance
that I will lose my job.
Krzys and Dion too.
        (Beat)
Even if management had
granted permission they
would need a lot more than
just your psychic say so
to justify bashing down a
wall... Albeit a very old and
dodgy one.

                    LAYLA
        So that's it we're just going
        to leave her here?

                    JACK
        I'm sorry but what do you
        want me to say?

                    LAYLA
               (To Mary)
        Mary please don't get upset.
        We know where you are now,
        we will get you out of there
        I promise.

Cordell inspects an area of the wall.
The brickwork looks unstable and parts
have crumbled.

                    CORDELL
        Do you carry a sledgehammer
        or such like in that van
        of yours?

                    JACK
        Yeah. Why?

CORDELL

The brickwork here doesn't
look too stable. In fact the
whole wall doesn't.

JACK

So.

CORDELL

Then I'm guessing it would
be fairly easy to bash a few
bricks out.

LAYLA

Yeah, now you're talking.

JACK

You got to be joking.
Knocking out bricks in an
old wall like this could
bring the whole bloody thing
crashing down on us.

CORDELL

All we need is enough space
to get the digi camera
in there.

                    JACK
No, it's far too risky...

                    LAYLA
That poor girl has lain
behind that wall for almost
a hundred and forty years...
That's a long, long time...
she didn't deserve to have
her life taken in such a
cruel and callous way. She
didn't deserve to be left
in there and be denied a
proper Christian burial from
a family who loved her.
A family who never knew
her fate.
          (Beat)
Please help her find peace and
reach her loved ones waiting
for her on the other side.

                    JACK
        I would love to, I really
        would. But I just can't
        go knocking holes in a
        crumbly old wall based on
        intel you claim was passed
        on by the spirit of a
        murdered woman...
                (Beat)
        I need more than that.

No sooner has Jack said his piece when a
loose brick in the wall dislodges itself and
falls to the ground, frightening the life
out of Jack and Cordell. Ad-lib reaction.

Another brick falls. Jack trains his torch
beam on the wall. A hole the size of two
bricks now appears.

                    JACK (Cont'd)
        What the fuck!?

                    CORDELL
        Wow!...

                    LAYLA
        Well done Mary.

                    JACK
          You have got to be
          kidding me.

Cordell wastes no time. He takes out a small
digital camera then climbs on top of the
Buffers. Holding the camera in one hand he
puts his arm through the hole in the wall
and begins taking random flash photos of the
cavity from as many angles as possible.

After a dozen or more he withdraws the
camera, switches it to view mode and starts
scrolling through the images.

                    CORDELL
          Oh my God...

PLATFORM.

Back on the platform, the rest of the group (minus Dion) are startled by a sudden high pitched Banshee like scream that emanates from the east tunnel. (Ad-lib reaction)

                    KRZYS
              (Curses in Polish)

                    FINLAY
          Sounded like a woman's scream.

                    SEAN
          It did didn't it.

                    CHARLIE
          Possibly a fox. Mating
          vixens sound just like a
          woman screaming.

                    FINLEY
          A fox! Oh please. What on
          earth would a fox be doing
          down here?

                    CHARLIE
          Looking for rats.

FINLAY

Yeah right. And maybe it
hangs out with the shadowy
hobo and they both go train
spotting.

KRZYS

That no fox. No animal make
sound like that.

SEAN

Whatever made it I don't
like the sound of it.
(Ponders)
I'm going to take a look.

Sean picks up a camcorder.

MARINA

On your own?

SEAN

It's a tunnel. What's the
worst that can happen?

KRZYS

You want me to come?

                    SEAN
          I'll be alright. I've got
          a radio. I'll call if I
          need you.

                    MARINA
          Shouldn't you wait for
          Cordell?

                    SEAN
          I won't be long. When he
          comes back give me a shout.

                    MARINA
          Okay. But be careful.

                    SEAN
          Don't worry. I'm a big boy.

Sean jumps down onto the track and starts
walking into the east tunnel.

WEST TUNNEL.

Dion is tentatively walking along the west tunnel on his own. He thinks he sees something up ahead. He pauses.

                    DION
          Jack... Cordell...
               (Beat)
          Is that you?
               (Beat)
          Jack... Cordell...

He cautiously moves a little further. All of a sudden there is a loud crackle and Krzys's voice booms out of the walkie talkie — making Dion jump. (Volume is set too high)

                    KRZYS (Over W/T)
          Krzys to Dion... Krzys to
          Dion. Please come over...

                    DION
               (Into radio)
          Hold on a sec.
               (Adjusts volume down)

                    KRZYS (Over W/T)
Is everything okay?...
Please over.

                    DION
Yeah mate fine. Still haven't
found them yet.

                    KRZYS (Over W/T)
Have you found the Jack and
others yet?... Please over...

                    DION
No, not yet.

                    KRZYS (Over W/T)
Maybe it sense for you to
come back... please over.

                    DION
Eh, I'll give it another
ten. If still no luck I'll
head back.

                    KRZYS (Over W/T)
Okay, but be taking care,
yes.

                    DION
          Will do... Cheers... I
          mean out.

Dion goes a little further. He comes to the
tunnel fork and stops to listen. He then
carries on into the right hand tunnel.

WEST TUNNEL. SIDING TUNNEL.

Jack, Cordell and Layla are making their
way back down the siding tunnel. Just
as the reach the fork junction, Dion
unexpectedly appears.

                    DION
          Where the bloody hell have
          you lot been?

Jack and Cordell jump out of their skins
(Ad-lib reaction) Layla on the other hand,
is unperturbed.

                    JACK
          Jesus Christ!!

                    DION
    Listen some really spooky
    shit went down in the
    other tunnel, you will not
    believe it.

                    LAYLA
    Didn't involve a disappearing
    train by any chance.

                    DION
    Yeah, how did you know?

                    LAYLA
    Brother you don't know half
    of it.

PLATFORM.

Everyone, with the exception of Sean, is
gathered around Cordell, who is holding a
iPad for all to see. The pictures reveal
what lies behind the cavity wall. The first
few pictures show the cavity and earth
illuminated by flash light.

The next frame reveals something both astonishing and terrifying. The crumpled, skeletal remains of a human being — still dressed in the tattered remnants of female garments.

Ad-lib reaction from everybody.

                    CORDELL
          Now is that totally awesome
          or what.

                    LAYLA
          Not so much for poor Mary
          though.

                    CORDELL
          Absolutely, but, with all due
          respect, it's still pretty
          bloody amazing!

                    FINLEY
          Awesome, absolutely awesome.

                    CORDELL
          Add together the train
          phenomena this is truly
          mind-blowing.

They all agree.

                    CORDELL (Cont'd)
          Fin did you manage to capture
          camera footage of the train?

                    FINLAY
          Eh, not really. A bit of
          sound that's all.

                    CHARLIE
          You screaming mostly.

                    FINLAY
          I thought I was going to
          be mangled under a train.
          Footage was hardly a
          priority.

                    CORDELL
          Jesus Fin!... A mind-blowing
          opportunity totally wasted.

                    FINLAY
          Did you then Cordell?

                    CORDELL
          Did I what?

                    FINLAY
          Capture any train footage at
          at your end?

                    CORDELL
          Eh, well, no.
               (Beat)
          In the chaos, you know.

                    FINLAY
          Two mind-blowing
          opportunities totally
          wasted then.

Digestive pause.

                    CHARLIE
          It's that poor girl that gets
          me. What sort of torment must
          she have gone through.

                    LAYLA
          I know honey but at least her
          suffering is almost over.

                    KRZYS
Vision of train unbelievable.
Now bone of tragic girl...
I knowing there something
about this place.

                    JACK
I still can't take it in.
Mind you fair play to Layla.
You led us to the girl's
body. My apologies for
doubting you.

                    LAYLA
If I had a Dollar every time
someone said that I'd be on
the cover of Forbes magazine.

                    DION
        (After beat)
So what are we going to do?

                    KRZYS
I am feeling very much
sadness for girl. We have
big duty to rescue her soul
- for her sake, for our sake
and for sake of God.

All agree, with the exception of.

                    MARINA
          Shouldn't we report this to
          the police first. I mean, if
          what Layla says is true we're
          talking about disturbing a
          crime scene.

                    DION
          I'm not being funny luv but
          it happened a hundred and
          forty years ago... Who are
          they going to arrest - Rip
          Van Winkle?

                    CORDELL
                 (After beat)
          We're all agreed then... Fin
          can you dial up Sean and
          get him back here. Dion and
          Krzys, can you go up top and
          bring back all the tools
          we need.

EAST TUNNEL.

Looking through the green camcorder screen for guidance, Sean is slowly edging his way along the tunnel. Rats scurry out of his way.

As he nears a bend he hears what sounds like a female sigh and stops to listen.

> SEAN
>
> Hello...

After a few moments he moves forward. Then the camcorder's infrared beam catches a movement up ahead.

> SEAN (Cont'd)
> Hello... Is anybody there?

He takes out an EMF Meter and begins to scan. Immediately it indicates the presence of a strong electromagnetic field up ahead.

PLATFORM.

Finlay calls Sean on the Walkie Talkie. Everyone in the group can hear.

> FINLAY
> Sean it's Fin. Do you copy, over?
> > (Beat)
> Fin to Sean. Do you copy, over?

> SEAN (Over W/T)
> > (After beat)
> Fin, Sean - over

> FINLAY
> Where are you?

> SEAN (Over W/T)
> Still in the Tunnel.

> FINLAY
> We need you back at base. Can you return ASAP?
> > (No response)
> Sean?...

                    SEAN (Over W/T)
There's something weird
going on.

                    FINLAY
Weird. What do you mean?
        (No response)
Sean... Sean...

                    SEAN (Over W/T)
I get the feeling that I am
not alone.

                    LAYLA
Not sure I like this.

                    FINLAY
Sean. Can you be more
specific?

                    SEAN (Over W/T)
        (After beat)
I can feel a presence of
some sort.

                    LAYLA
I'm getting a bad vibe.
Tell him to stop and get
his ass back here now!

Cordell takes over radio from Fin

> CORDELL
> Sean this is Cordell, please
> ignore and head back to base
> ASAP. Repeat. Ignore and head
> back to base ASAP — over.
>> (Beat, beat)
> Sean do you copy?... over.

> SEAN (Over W/T)
>> (Starts to crackle)
> Hold on minute, I think I see
> something...
>> (Beat)
> What the!!

A high pitch banshee like scream is heard
through the W/T. Momentary pause followed by
shocked reaction. Ad-lib.

> CORDELL
> SEAN!!... SEAN!!

Apart from a strange electrostatic
crackling, Sean's radio is silent.
Bewildered group reaction.

EXT. DISUSED UNDERGROUND STATION. NIGHT.

Krzys and Dion are in the back of the Transit van. They remove a sledge hammer and a pick axe, a holdall of assorted tools and a large cloth sheet.

Krzys locks the rear cargo doors and the pair carry the tools into the station.

LATER. EAST TUNNEL.

Five of the group, Jack, Cordell, Layla, Finlay and Charlie are in the east tunnel looking for Sean. They call his name and try to contact him on the radio.

> LAYLA
> I am feeling a strong
> presence.

> CORDELL
> Who?

> LAYLA
> Another entity. A Woman.

                    CORDELL
        Edith?.

LATER. FURTHER ALONG EAST TUNNEL.

Inching their way along the east tunnel,
the group come to a fork where the tunnel
splits into two.

                    CORDELL
        Another siding?

                    JACK
        No, the left is the old
        Shoreditch spur line.

                    CORDELL
        What do you think Layla?

                    LAYLA
        Not so sure. I feel great
        energy from both.

                    CORDELL
        Okay, I think it best we
        split.

                    FINLAY
          Is that a good idea?

                    CORDELL
          Have you a better suggestion?

                    FINLAY
          Yes. We stick together.

                    JACK
          We've all got a radio. If
          we stay in contact what's
          the problem?

                    FINLAY
          Sean's got a radio.

                    JACK
          He was on his own though.

                    CHARLIE
          It's coming up to two forty
          five AM. No matter what
          happens I suggest we meet
          back here at three fifteen.
          If we haven't found Sean by
          then... well...

All agree. Finlay reluctantly.

                    CORDELL
          Okay, Jack and I will take
          the left tunnel. Layla, Fin
          and Charlie you go right.

                    JACK
          Be careful, stick close
          together and stay in contact,
          okay.

The two groups split and go their separate
ways into the cold dark tunnels.

RIGHT TUNNEL.

                    CHARLIE
          Jesus it's absolutely
          freezing in here.

                    LAYLA
          The vibes aren't good...
          Not good at all. So
          much negativity.

Finlay's reaction. It isn't what he wants
to hear.

LATER.

A little further on, Charlie's torch beam highlights a recess in the tunnel wall. In the recess there are a dozen or so steps leading down to a door. A scurrying rat draws her attention away and she continues walking forward - with Fin close behind.

Layla, who is lagging at the rear goes to the recess and looks in. Lurking in the shadow of her torch beam is a male human form.

> LAYLA
> I thought it was you...

Looking pale, frightened and bewildered, Sean steps partially into the light.

> LAYLA (Cont'd)
> What are you doing hiding
> in there? We're all looking
> for you.
> > (Beat)
> Are you alright?

Sean slowly steps out and is illuminated by Layla's torch beam.

                    SEAN
I don't think so.
        (Beat)
I feel really strange...
Frightened... Cold.

                    LAYLA
That's to be expected.

                    SEAN
I've really screwed up
haven't I?

                    LAYLA
It's not your fault.

                    SEAN
I have let everyone down.
        (Beat)
Cordell's going to be really
pissed off isn't he?

                    LAYLA
He'll get over it.
        (Beat)
Now come on back to us.
This isn't your time.

                    FINLAY
              (After beat, to Layla)
         Eh — who are you talking to?

                    LAYLA
         Sean.

                    FINLAY
         What?

A couple of yards ahead, Charlie's torch
beam scans from left to right, illuminating
the claustrophobic gloom. She turns 90
degrees to look at the space at the side
of her and is instantly sent reeling by
the unexpected and horrific sight of Sean's
deathly pale face - frozen in an expression
of sheer terror... Charlie screams.

LATER. RIGHT TUNNEL.

All five are standing around Sean's pale rigid body. All are in a state of deep shock - especially Charlie. Ad-lib comments, etc.

> CORDELL
> Is he dead? Check his pulse!

Jack feels Sean's neck for a pulse.

> JACK
> I can't feel anything.
> (Beat)
> I think he's gone!

Shocked reaction, ad-lib, etc.

Without warning, as if jolted back to life, Sean gasps in a mouthful of air, startling the crap out of everybody.

> CORDELL
> Jesus, he's alive!

With his eyes still staring open wide Sean begins to shake and twitch, similar to an epileptic fit. Jack immediately responds by putting him in the recovery position.

                    FINLAY
          What the hell's happening
          to him?

                    JACK
          He's having some sort of
          seizure. Is he epileptic?

                    CORDELL
          Not that I know of...
          Anyone?

Ad-lib, no one knows/not sure, etc. After a few moments he begins to calm slightly but is clearly very disturbed.

                    CORDELL (Cont'd)
          Sean, what is it. What
          happened to you?

Sean tries to talk but his efforts are slurred and incomprehensible.

                    CHARLIE
          We have got to get him
          out of here now. He needs
          medical attention.

All agree.

                    CORDELL
          Charlie's right. We got to
          get him to a hospital ASAP.

                    JACK
     Shit!

                    CORDELL
          I realise this puts you in a
          very awkward position Jack
          but we clearly have no other
          choice.

                    JACK
          I know, I know...
               (Beat)
          Why the fuck did I ever get
          involved in this!

                    CHARLIE
               (To Jack)
          It's not your fault.

                    JACK
          Yeah, you try telling
          that to my boss and the
          transport police.

                    LAYLA
               (After beat)
          There's only one person to
          blame for this and all the
          years of misery...

Layla bends down and picks up Sean's
video camera.

                    LAYLA
          The evil that is Edith
          Rattray.

Group reaction.

PLATFORM.

Back at the platform the entire group have gathered as Cordell rewinds the footage from Sean's camcorder. The mood is quiet and intense.

Sean is sitting down in a corner, knees in chest and shaking. His mind lost somewhere else. Marina covers him with a warm jacket, adding to the fleece already over him.

Cordell hits playback on the camera Sean was carrying, revealing the captured footage on the viewing screen.

We see from the Camcorder point of view as Sean inches his way through the tunnel (using camcorder viewer to see) whilst talking to Cordell on the radio. (Ref page 128)

Sean's (unsteady) camcorder footage has captured the manifestation of a dark creeping mist that is slowly advancing towards him.

What unfolds on screen shocks them all. Quickly and unexpectedly, an ashen female face, full demonic menace, manifests out of the pitch black screaming like a banshee.

The footage then becomes chaotic. It settles after the camera is dropped to the ground. The group react with a mixture of stunned incredulity and horror. Speechless, they each look at one another. Ad-lib, etc

> CORDELL
> Oh-my-God. What just
> happened?
> > (Beat)
> I just can't believe it.

> LAYLA
> Edith Sybil Rattray... One
> seriously fucked up bitch.

> FINLAY
> That's it, I'm out of here.
> I'm not staying in this place
> one minute longer!

Jack and Krzys agree.

CORDELL

What!?

JACK

Right this is over. I want you
all out NOW! So please pack
up your gear and make for the
exit as soon as you can.

CORDELL

Hold on, hold on. I know
you've had a terrible shock,
we all have — but think of
the amazing opportunity we
have here.

FINLAY

Opportunity? After what's
happened to Sean, I'm not
hanging around for the same
to happen to me.

CORDELL

I thought you wanted to
prove 'conclusively' the
existence of the paranormal
to the world.

FINLAY

I do. But I don't want to
die doing it.

CORDELL

But this is mega. Think about
it. It's going to go viral!

JACK

Fuck viral Cordell. I am not
risking the safety of anyone
else down here. I'm in deep
enough shit as it is.

CHARLIE

But why did this entity
attack Sean? Why is she so
angry with us?

FINLAY

Oh entity is it now. What
happened to the 'homeless
person' theory?

CORDELL

Whoever, whatever. Don't
you want to find out?

                    JACK
        We all do Cordell but it's
        just too bloody risky.

                    FINLAY
        I agree. If you want to stay
        here and find out why the bitch
        from beyond attacked Sean, good
        luck to you... but I'm off.

Digestive pause.

                    LAYLA
        If you want to know the
        answer, It's got something
        to do with Mary.

EXT. STREET. LONDON. NIGHT. 1882.

On a rain swept street corner in Victorian
London, Stalker and Janus are taking shelter
under a shop front awning. Moments later
Randolph Morton's shiny black horse drawn
carriage pulls up across the street.

Emerson the driver gets down and runs
across the road to where Stalker and Janus
are waiting.

                    EMERSON
     Tommy. Billy. What a night eh.
          (Beat)
     So, anyway — is it done?

                    MR JANUS
     You know it is — I've already
     fucking told you.

                    EMERSON
     I know, I know, it's just
     that the boss wants it
     confirmed that's all.

                    STALKER
     The girl's disappeared and
     ain't never coming back. I
     guarantee it... So with that
     in mind, we want what's owed.

                    EMERSON
     Fair do's.

Emerson reaches into the inside pocket of
his rain soaked overcoat and pulls out a
cash filled envelope. He then gives it to Mr
Stalker who checks the amount.

                    EMERSON (Cont'd)
        Amount as agreed... And eh.

                    MR STALKER
        Don't worry you'll get
        your cut.

                    EMERSON
        Smashing... I'd best be
        passing on the good news
        then.

Stalker and Janus acknowledge Emerson with
a cursory nod. Emerson then promptly walks
back across to the carriage.

EXT. STREET. CARRIAGE. LONDON. NIGHT. 1882.

Emerson approaches Morton's carriage and
knocks on the door window. The widow slides
down a few inches.

                    EMERSON
        It's done.

We hear a muffled voice from within the cab.

                    EMERSON (Cont'd)
        I can assure you when Mr
        Stalker says it's done,
        it's done.

The cab door window is abruptly pulled shut.

INT. CARRIAGE. LONDON. NIGHT. 1882.

As the carriage moves away we see that the
only passenger within is Edith Rattray —
immersed in a look of cold hearted fulfilment.

INT. DISUSED UNDERGRND STATION. PRESENT DAY.

Resume. various startled Ad-lib comments,
etc, from group,

                    CORDELL
        Wow! So Morton had nothing
        to do with Mary's murder
        after all?

                    LAYLA
        It was all Edith. And now we
        have discovered her hidden
        secret she's not best pleased.

                    LAYLA (Cont'd)
Even in death she carried
on her hateful revenge.
Fifty two men including
your friend.

                    JACK
Marty. What did he do? I
don't understand?

                    LAYLA
Apart from Mary, all of
her victims have been men.
Unfaithful men. Somehow she
knows and punishes them.

                    KRZYS
Maybe it now make kind of
sense. She hear the Marty
talk about cheat on wife and
want to punish him too.

                    JACK
Who knows.

CORDELL

Wow! This story gets more
bizarre and fantastic by the
minute. You couldn't make
it up!

CHARLIE

Even I'll admit it... That's
if it's true of course.

KRZYS

But who will believe us? I
see with own eye and I not
believe. It is crazy.

JACK

Interesting as all this may
be we've still got Sean to
think about. We need to get
him to a doctor.

LAYLA

What are we going to do
about Mary? We still got to
get her out of that tomb.

                    JACK
      Look, whatever happens, I
      promise to see she is brought
      out of there as soon as
      possible. At least she's been
      found, that's the main thing.
          (Beat)
      Now all of you, please,
      get your stuff and make for
      the exit.

SHORT WHILE LATER.

As the group make their way towards the exit they experience a mild ground tremor that stops them in their tracks. Layla looks towards the east tunnel. Ad-lib group reaction and comments, etc.

Approximately 20 seconds later there is another, more aggressive tremor, during which the main lights go out, plunging the platform into total darkness momentarily before the backup lanterns kick in.

That is followed by a third which literally shakes the walls and causes the already crumbling structure around the exit arch to come crashing down, blocking the way out.

When the dust cloud finally clears Jack, Krzys and Dion rush to evaluate using torchlight. The others join them.

                    KRZYS
          Oh shit. What we do now? It
          look like we trap.

                    JACK
          I don't fucking believe this.
               (Beat)
          Where are the tools you got?

                    DION
          They're over there.

                    KRZYS
          But we going to need more than
          hammer and pick to move this.

                    JACK
          It's better than nothing.

                    CORDELL
          We are going to be able to
          get out aren't we?

                     JACK
          Eventually yes, but it'll
          take a good couple of hours.
          That's if we all pitch in.

                    FINLAY
          Isn't there another way out?

                     JACK
          Not unless you are prepared
          to walk out through the
          tunnels.
               (Beat)
          Three miles west or two
          miles east.

                    FINLAY
          No way am I going back in
          those tunnels.

Ad-lib comment, etc.

CHARLIE
But surely we would be
alright if we stuck
close together?

LAYLA
(After beat)
We too late for that now.

As if on cue, a eerie cold air current
blows out of the east tunnel and envelops
the platform area. The battery lanterns
then fade and die one by one. concerned
group reaction.

LAYLA
She's coming....
(Beat)
All of you gather behind
me NOW!
(Beat)
Quick as you can.

The group quickly form up behind Layla and wait. Then as the EVP and motion detectors start going crazy, the group gasp as a dark mist enters from the east tunnel and slowly manifests into the spectral form of a Victorian woman - who simply stands and stares.

                    MARINA
          Look! The tunnel. Someone is
          standing there!

                    KRZYS
          My god!

Cordell immediately points his camcorder and starts to record.

                    LAYLA
          Edith Rattray.

Ad-lib reaction as Edith stands and stares with great menace. A few moments later she moves (floats/hovers) up onto the platform and begins to move slowly closer, her hateful stare fixated on Layla and the group.

                    CORDELL
          Oh my god this is mega! This
          is mega!

                    CHARLIE
          This cannot be happening.

About half way towards the speechless
ghost hunters, Edith stops again, allowing
us to see a close up of her for the
first time. She is spectral white all over
apart from her pinned up jet black hair
and her hate filled piercing jet black
eyes, deeply set in a gaunt ashen face
with high pronounced cheek bones.

                    LAYLA
               (To Edith, loud)
          EDITH RATTRAY!...
               (Beat)
          WE KNOW WHO YOU ARE...
          WE KNOW WHAT YOU HAVE DONE.

                    FINLAY
          Are you insane?

                    LAYLA
          I ain't scared of her.
          Marina, get that picture
          of Edith for me. Quick as
          you can.

Marina does as she is asked. She quickly
goes to a rucksack, removes Edith's portrait
photo from a folder and hands it to Layla.

                    LAYLA (Cont'd)
          WELL... WHAT ARE YOU WAITING
          FOR EDITH!?

Edith does nothing, she just keeps on
silently staring.

                    LAYLA (Cont'd)
          I get it. You just like to
          frighten, hurt and kill
          people who can't fight back.
          That's very courageous
          of you.

Still Edith does nothing but stare. Layla
removes a candle from her jacket pocket.

                    LAYLA (Cont'd)
You have a lot of pain and
anger don't you Edith? Why
is that?
        (Beat, beat)
You were a big west end
star, an honoured member of
high society, with fame and
fortune... What happened
Edith, what happened that
made you to take your
own life?
        (Beat)
I mean, jumping in front of a
train and being mangled under
its wheels is a pretty nasty
way to go?

Edith maintains her hateful stare.

                    LAYLA (Cont'd)
Tell me Edith. Why do you
have so much rage? Why so
much hate?

INT. OFFICE. THEATRE. LONDON. DAY. 1883.

Edith walks in to Randolph Morton's office and is appalled to find Morton, semi naked, having sex with a young female employee who is bent over his desk.

With Morton as equally shocked, an enraged Edith grabs a metal letter opener from the desk and launches a screaming frenzied attack, stabbing widely at Morton and the girl.

Morton, with trousers and under garments down around his ankles, receives a number of wounds to his hands, arms and upper body. He staggers and falls to floor - blood flowing freely.

The girl having received a couple of deep flesh wounds manages to escape screaming for help. With Randolph incapacitated, Edith continues her vicious onslaught until a blood soaked Morton loses consciousness.

As the red mist lifts Edith discards the knife upon the realisation of what she has done. Having responded to the screams for help, two members of staff rush into the office.

Edith, covered in Randolph's blood, hastily barges past and flees.

EXT. THEATRE. LONDON. DAY. 1883.

A blood soaked Edith exits the stage door and rushes into the street. She is confused and not sure what to do. Immediately behind her a small group of male theatre staff exit onto the street in hot pursuit. Edith runs.

One of the staff members hails a POLICE CONSTABLE who happens to be walking past. We see him speak excitedly to the officer then point towards Edith as she runs down the street. The Policeman blows his whistle several times then joins in the chase.

EXT. BROOM ST UNDERGRND STN. DAY. 1883.

With the men and police catching up, and startled onlookers staring, a clearly exhausted Edith pauses momentarily to weigh her options. She then bolts into Broom Street underground station.

INT. BROOM ST UNDERGROUND STN. DAY. 1883.

Edith runs past the ticket kiosk, roughly pushing her way past unwary rail travellers. At the ticket gate she desperately barges past the ticket inspector, through the gate and along the tunnel that leads to the spiral stair case.

PLATFORM. 1883.

Edith enters the platform. Aware that she has been followed, she frantically pushes past waiting passengers and makes her way to the end of the platform in a bid to find another escape route. All she finds though is a dead end with no alternative exit.

At the platform entrance a commotion ensues as two policemen, three theatre staff and an angry ticket collector, start searching for Edith. As an approaching train rumbles through the east tunnel towards the platform, she is spotted.

Cornered and with no way out, Edith decides to jump off the platform into the path of the train.

INT. DISUSED UNDERGRND STN. PRESENT DAY.

Resume. Edith is still in same position and still staring.

>   LAYLA
>   I am sorry that your life
>   had to end that way. But no
>   amount of jealousy, no amount
>   of anger is justification for
>   the many sacred lives you
>   have taken... Lives that were
>   not yours to take, regardless
>   of their sins...

                    LAYLA (Cont'd)
          Your husband, fifty two men
          over a hundred years and
          the cold callous murder of
          Mary Elwes.
                    (Beat)
          Your time is over Edith
          Rattray. You are no longer
          wanted here. It is time
          for you to move on and be
          judged for your malicious and
          murderous sins.

Showing strength and confidence, Layla locks
eyes with Edith and with a burning candle
in one hand and Edith's portrait print in
the other, she starts walking towards her.

Edith doesn't budge but her eyes evoke even
more anger as Layla presses her challenge.

                    LAYLA (Cont'd)
          I command you to go now from
          this moment, from this day,
          from this place!... I command
          you to go now from this time,
          from this dimension, from
          this world!

                    LAYLA (Cont'd)
              (Beat)
          Be gone restless spirit of
          Edith Sybil Rattray. Be gone
          forever and never return!!

Layla, using the candle, sets fire to the
printed copy of Edith's portrait, holds it
for a few seconds, then throws it down onto
the ground as it burns to ashes.

Moments later, Edith's evil countenance
subsides and to everyone's great
astonishment, and relief, her ethereal
figure begins to withdraw and dissolve. It
slowly loses form and returns to the dark
mist before breaking up and disappearing
altogether. Ad-lib reaction from group.

                    CORDELL
          WOW! Was that totally bloody
          surreal or what. I have never
          seen anything like it!

                    JACK
          That was easy?

                    LAYLA
A bit too easy. I at least
expected her to put up some
sort of fight.

                    FINLAY
Where did she go. Was it
into the light?

                    LAYLA
The Light. That evil bitch.
I don't think so.

                    CHARLIE
Then where?

                    LAYLA
Don't rightly know. Wherever
evil bitches go I guess.

                    DION
That was seriously fucked up.
I almost crapped my pants.

                    KRZYS
Me too also.

We focus on Marina. Something above catches her eye. She looks above her and screams. Everyone looks up and are horrified to see Edith floating above them looking meaner and more evil than ever.

Screaming like a Banshee, Edith launches herself down at Layla and grabs her around the throat with her long bony fingers. Layla tries her best to fight back but such is the strength of Edith's energy she is gradually overwhelmed.

The group can only stand back and look on in horror as Layla falls to her knees as the life is literally squeezed out of her. Then, just as Layla is about to pass into unconsciousness an ethereal voice speaks to Edith.

                    MARY
          Leave her be you
          murderous bitch!

A small orb of light slowly manifests into the spiritual form of a twenty something year old woman dressed in Victorian period clothing, allowing us to see Mary Elwes spirit for the first time.

Slightly taken aback, Edith momentarily loosens her grip allowing Layla some brief respite.

                    MARY
              (More assertive)
          Let her be I said!

Undeterred Edith resumes her grip. Seconds later a second orb manifests into the spiritual form of the businessman who was pushed off the platform in the 1950s (Page 3)

                 BUSINESSMAN
          You heard her. Let her go. NOW!

Shock and awe reaction from group. Edith is even more taken aback and again loosens her grip. Then another orb reveals itself - a SOLDIER from world war 1.

                   SOLDIER
          I really would if I were you.

Slightly bewildered, Edith releases her grip on Layla who slithers unconscious to the ground. With body language exuding menace, Edith slowly advances towards the spectral trio who have dared to challenge her.

As she does however, another orb appears... Then, one by one, 52 of Edith's past male victims, spanning several decades, social class and age, manifest and encircle her.

Edith attempts to act defiant but it soon dawns on her that she is no longer in control and her intimidating posture quickly changes to one of apprehension.

The enclave of spirits surrounding Edith move forward in unison, tightening the ring around her. Edith's now fearful countenance and body language begs forgiveness but her pleas go ignored.

The ring finally closes around Edith merging into one powerful spiritual entity. Realising her fate Edith shrieks out a final scream before being engulfed and absorbed into the shimmering ball of light.

The ball then shrinks into a football sized orb that momentarily hovers before rising and fading to nothing.

Ad-lib reaction from group. They are too stunned and amazed to utter a word. They then go to assist Layla who is beginning to come too.

                    CHARLIE
          Layla. Are you alright!?

                    LAYLA
          I think so.

From the ceiling a tennis ball size orb appears and floats down. Just before reaching the platform it manifests into the ethereal form of Mary.

                    LAYLA (Cont'd)
                 (To Mary)
          The bitch gone?

Mary nods affirmatively.

                    LAYLA (Cont'd)
          Thank you Mary.

                    (Beat)
              Couldn't have done it
              without you.

Mary smiles warmly.

                    LAYLA (Cont'd)
              Don't worry. I will, I
              promise. If it's the last
              thing I do.

Mary mouths the words thank you to all and
waves goodbye. Her form morphs back into an
orb, after which it floats off and disappears.

More stunned ad-lib reaction.

                    CORDELL
              (After beat)
              For any reason that isn't on
              video. I will kill myself.

EXT. GRAVEYARD. DORSET. ENGLAND. DAY.

In a small Dorset village graveyard near to a very old church, everyone involved in the tunnel ghost hunt has gathered at an open grave to pay their last respects to Mary.

Sean has recovered but looks gaunt and no longer appears as confident as he once was.

A VICAR is present along with a half dozen FAMILY MEMBERS, including an old man, RICHARD ELWES. After the Vicar gives a typical Church of England blessing, the coffin is lowered into the grave.

>   CORDELL
> I am pleased you didn't
> lose your job.

>   JACK
> It was touch and go at first
> but thanks to you my bosses
> decided to make use of
> the publicity.

>   CORDELL
> Two faced bastards.

                    JACK
            (After beat)
I hear you went viral.

                  CORDELL
It's mental. Twenty million
views and counting. A month
ago we were nothing, now
we're the biggest thing
on YouTube.

                    JACK
My daughter's in seventh
heaven. A month ago I was
daddy boring, now I'm
daddy cool.
            (After beat)
So all these folk are related
to Mary?

                  CORDELL
They are indeed. The old
chap in the trilby is
Richard Elwes, her great,
great nephew. The rest are
his family.

                    JACK
How did you manage to track
him down?

                    CORDELL
Geneology.com. It was fairly
easy to be honest.

                    JACK
Either way you've done her
proud. Wherever she is I'm
sure she appreciates it.

                    CORDELL
It's the least we could do...

Layla is standing next to a polished black
headstone. A close-up reads.

            IN LOVING MEMORY OF A DEAR
               DAUGHTER AND SISTER.
            MARY ELIZABETH ELWES
               BORN SEPT 1ST 1854
         LOST JUNE 26TH 1882 AGED 28 YRS.
               FOUND MAY ^{15th} 2022

               REUNITED WITH LOVE
             MAY YOU REST IN PEACE.

On top of the headstone is a small orb of light. It rises and hovers momentarily.

                    LAYLA
          So pleased you're happy...
          So long Mary...

The orb floats towards the sky. Layla follows it with her eyes until it fades. She smiles contentedly.

FADE.

                    THE END

Printed in Great Britain
by Amazon

82384961R00103